THOMAS'S COUNTING BOOK

Tony Wells

HEINEMANN · LONDON

1

One engine having a drink.

2

Two engines at the harbour.

3

Three engines race each other.

4

Four engines at the turntable.

5

Five engines by the sea.

6

Six engines being mended.

7

Seven engines in the snow.

8

Eight engines see the Queen.

9

Nine engines go to sleep.

10

Ten engines at the party.

How many engines in the shed?

Here are the twin engines.

How many are there?

How many engines can you see?

How many of them are painted blue?

William Heinemann Ltd
Michelin House
81 Fulham Road
London SW3 6RB

LONDON   MELBOURNE   AUCKLAND

First published 1987
Reprinted 1989, 1990 (twice)
Copyright © William Heinemann Ltd 1987

ISBN 0 434 92773 2

Printed in Belgium by
Proost International Book Production